هِبَةُ وَكوكو

Adam
Grow healthy and
happy

With love
Olivia and Gabriel

OXFORD
UNIVERSITY PRESS

تَعيشُ هِبَةُ في الإماراتِ مَعَ عائِلَتِها.

تُحِبُّ هِبَةُ أَنْ تَتَكَلَّمَ
مَعَ جَدَّتِها في لُبْنانَ
وَتُخْبِرَها عَنْ بَبَّغائِها الصَّغيرِ كوكو.

تُحِبُّ هِبَةُ كوكو كَثيراً.

وَكوكو يُحِبُّها أَيْضاً.

عِنْدَما تَذْهَبُ هِبَةُ إِلى مَدْرَسَتِها،

تُحِبُّ أَنْ تُخْبِرَ أَصْدِقاءَها عَنْ كوكو.

في أَحَدِ الْأَيّامِ، كانَتْ هِبَةُ تَلْعَبُ مَعَ كوكو.

كانَ أَبوها يَتَكَلَّمُ بِالْهاتِفِ مَعَ جَدَّتِها.

قَالَتْ هِبَةُ: ماذا حَصَلَ يا أَبي؟

قالَ أَبوها: جَدَّتُكِ مَريضَةٌ وَيَجِبُ أَنْ نَزورَها في لُبْنانَ،

أَمّا كوكو فَسَيَبْقى عِنْدَ الْجيرانِ.

حَزِنَتْ هِبَةُ وَبَدَأَتْ بِالْبُكاءِ.

قالَ أَبوها: لا تَقْلَقي يا حَبيبَتي.

سَوْفَ تَكونُ جَدَّتُكِ بِخَيْرٍ.

وَسَيَكونُ كوكو بِأَمانٍ أَيْضاً.

اِذْهَبي الْآنَ إِلى فِراشِكِ لِكَيْ تَنامي.

اِلْتَفَتَتْ هِبَةُ نَحْوَ كوكو وَقالَتْ: سَأُسافِرُ غَداً إِلى لُبْنانَ لِأَزورَ جَدَّتي وَأَطْمَئِنَّ عَلَيْها. لَنْ أَسْتَطيعَ أَنْ أَعْتَنِيَ بِكَ.

رَكَضَتْ هِبَةُ إِلى غُرْفَتِها وَهِيَ حَزِينَةٌ.

قالَ كوكو: يا هِبَةُ، يا هِبَةُ!

هَيّا اسْتَيقِظي يا صَديقَتي

نَهَضَتْ هِبَةُ مِنْ سَريرِها فَرَأَتْ كوكو بِجانِبِها.

قالَتْ هِبَةُ: أَهَذا أَنْتَ يا كوكو، ماذا حَصَلَ؟

قالَ كوكو: أَنا ذاهِبٌ وَلا أُريدُ أَنْ يَعْتَنِيَ بي أَحَدٌ آخَرُ،

فَأَنا أُحِبُّكِ أَنْتِ.

قَالَتْ هِبَةُ: وَأَنا أُحِبُّكَ أَيْضاً وَأُرِيدُ أَنْ أَعْتَنِيَ بِكَ.

سَأَكُونُ حَزِينَةً جِدّاً إِذا ذَهَبْتَ.

قالَ كوكو: أَنْتِ ذاهِبَةٌ لِزِيارَةِ جَدَّتِكِ وَلَنْ تَكوني مَعي.

بَكَتْ هِبَةُ كَثيراً، فَهِيَ لا تُريدُ الذَّهابَ مِنْ دُونِ كوكو.

دَخَلَ أَبو هِبَةَ إلى غُرْفَتِها وَقالَ: اِسْتَيْقِظي يا هِبَةُ!

قالَتْ هِبَةُ: يا أَبي، يا أَبي! أَيْنَ كوكو؟

أُريدُ أَنْ أَبْقى هُنا لِكَيْ أَعْتَنِيَ بِهِ.»

قالَ أَبوها:

كوكو هُنا وَسَوْفَ يَأْتي مَعَنا في الطّائِرَةِ،
فَقَدِ اشْتَرَيْتُ لَهُ تَذْكِرَةً خاصَّةً.

نَظَرَتْ هِبَةُ إلى أَبيها وَقالَتْ: شُكْراً يا أَبي أُحِبُّكَ كَثيراً.

وَضَعَتْ هِبَةُ كوكو في السَّيَّارَةِ
وَقالَتْ لَهُ: الْحَمْدُ لِلَّهِ كُنْتُ أَحْلُمُ فَقَطْ.
سَوْفَ تَأْتي مَعَنا وَسَتَرى جَدَّتي أَيْضاً.

نالية إرشادات تساعد في نجاح درس القراءة الموجّهة. استخدام صيغة الأمر المفرد هنا سببه أنّ كل معلّم ب مع أعمار وقدرات التلاميذ باللغة العربية، بالإضافة إلى ما يقومون به في الفصل (صيغة المذكّر استخدمت ، ومكوّناتها بدقّة في جميع دروس القراءة الموجّهة. امنح التلاميذ الوقت ليفكّروا بالأسئلة ويجيبوا عليها. قدّم حـل المشكلات. عد إلى استراتيجيّة التحقّق بعد القراءة المستقلّة. تقدّم طرق التدريس هذه دعماً لسلوكيّات شطاء ومتحمّسين للقراءة.

١ قدّم تهيئة لموضوع الكتاب:

اقرأ العنوان جهراً مع المرور بسرعة وانسيابية بإصبعك تحت الكلمات أثناء القراءة. اطلب من التلاميذ قراءة العنوان جهراً أيضاً. اجعلهم يحدّدون اسمي هبة وكوكو. "هبة تحبّ كوكو كثيراً، تحبّ أن تأخذه معها في كلّ مكان."

٢ قدّم تمهيداً للكتاب فاسحاً المجال للتلاميذ لإعطاء توقعات مفضّلة عن موضوع القصّة:

الصفحة ٢: "تتحدّث هبة لأحد ما على كمبيوترها اللوحي (تابلت)؛ مع من تتحدّث يا ترى؟ هل هناك أيّ إشارة تدلّنا إلى المكان الذي تعيش فيه جدّتها؟ هل لاحظتم أيّ كلمة هنا تساعدنا لنعرف إن كان هذا صحيحاً؟

نستطيع أن نرى كم تحبّ هبة كوكو - حتّى أنّه بجانبها عندما كانت تتحدّث مع جدّتها."

الصفحة ٤: "هل تعتقدون أن هبة في المدرسة الآن؟ هل تعتقدون أنها مشتاقة لكوكو؟"

الصفحة ٦: "لاحظت أن أبا هبة يتحدّث على الهاتف. يبدو أنّه حصل شيء ما. هبة منزعجة جدّاً. ماذا يمكن أن يكون؟"

الصفحة ١٠: "ماذا يحصل هنا برأيكم؟" إذا لم يعرف التلاميذ من الصورة أنه كان حلماً، قل لهم مشيراً إلى حواف الصورة المتعرّجة التي تدلّ على ذلك وأنّ هبة كانت في السـرير.

لا تستمر في التقديم للقصّة ولكن أوجد هدفاً للقراءة من "هيّا نعيد التحضير للقراءة. أتمنّى أن يحدث شيء ما يوقف انزعاج هبة."

٣ حضّر للتراكيب النحويّة المتوقّعة:

للتحضير للتراكيب الأقل شيوعاً والتي يمكن أن تكون غير مألوفة، ركّز على 'ماذا حصل؟' في الصفحة ٢. و'أهذا أنت؟' في الصفحة ١٠ و'حزنت' في الصفحة ٧.

عزّز التغييرات التي حصلت للجذر 'ذ/هـ/ب'، "هيّا ننظر إلى كلمة 'اذهبي'. جذر هذه الكلمة هو ذ/هـ/ب. لنجد بعض الكلمات الأخرى في الكتاب والتي اشتقّت من ذ/هـ/ب. أثناء إيجاد التلاميذ لهذه الكلمات اطلب منهم أن يشرحوا لماذا تغيّرت؟ 'ذاهب' - ناقش أن هذه الكلمة هي اسم الفاعل، تظهر أنّ كوكو هو من يذهب. 'ذاهبة' - ناقش معهم أن هذه الكلمة هي اسم الفاعل، وأنها تحتوي على 'ـةً' في نهاية الكلمة لأنّها تعود على هبة ويجب أن تكون بصيغة المؤنث. 'الذهاب' - ناقش معهم أنّ هذه الكلمة هي مصد وهذا الجذر والتي تعني 'أن يذهب/تذهب'. في حال احتاج التلاميذ للدعم في تحديد الكلمات - "هل يمكن أن ترى كيف اشتقّت هذه الكلمات من الجذر ذ/هـ/ب وصنعت كلمات مختلفة بمعان مختلفة تعود لبعضها في المعنى."

"في بعض الأحيان تنضم بعض الحروف والكلمات معاً." أشر إلى 'فسيبقى' في الصفحة ٦ واطلب من التلاميذ أن يعثروا عليها في كتبهم. "ما هي الأجزاء الثلاثة هنا؟" أعط التلاميذ بعض الوقت ليفكّروا في السؤال وادعمهم إذا لـزم الأمر. "إذاً هي؟ 'فـ/سـ/يبقى'".

"الآن انظروا إلى كلمة 'وسترى' في الصفحة ١٥." أشر إلى الكلمة واطلب من التلاميذ أن يعثروا عليها في كتبهم. "ما هي الأجزاء الثلاثة هنا؟ (و/سـ/ترى). هل يمكن أن تعثروا على كلمات أخرى تشبهها في الكتاب؟" مثلاً: 'وسيكون' في الصفحة ٧، و'فهي' في الصفحة ١١ و'سأسافر' في الصفحة ٨. (الهدف هنا هو أن يبدأ التلاميذ بملاحظة أجزاء الكلمات وليس الهدف أن يتعمّقوا في المعلومة.)

Haunted Ba

by Rupert Matthews

A Screaming Warrior

RIGHT: *Sir William Waller who commanded the Parliamentary forces at the Battle of Lansdown.*

Freezing Hill is well named, for the winter winds blow cold on this exposed hill. But it is not just the cold which can send a shiver down your spine. On still summer evenings the sounds of battle echo across the high ground. Swords clash on swords, horses neigh and men yell. Suddenly a headless man may lurch out of the darkness, grasping frantically at empty air before vanishing into the night.

These terrifying phantoms date back to the English Civil War. In July 1643 a force of Royalist troops attempted to storm into Bath, a strategic city loyal to Parliament. Led jointly by Prince Maurice, Prince Rupert's brother, the Marquess of Hertford and Sir Ralph Hopton, the 6,000-strong Royalists were composed largely of Cornishmen.

Marching south from Chard, the Royalists encountered the Parliamentarians on Freezing Hill, and drove them south to entrenched artillery positions on Lansdown Hill, where the main Roundhead force of 7,000 men under Sir William Waller was dug in. There the hard-fought battle degenerated into a savage killing contest which lasted until midnight. The resulting stalemate lasted until the Royalists retreated, and Bath remained with Parliament. A fine monument to Sir Bevil Grenville, a Royalist officer killed around dusk, marks the battlefield today.

Lurking around the site of the old city walls, in Upper Borough Walls, is another phantom of Civil War vintage. Far less startling than the bloody apparitions of Freezing

BELOW: *A monument marks the spot on Lansdown Hill where Sir Bevil Grenville fell.*

Hill, this ghost takes the form of a rather grubby workman. One witness thought the man needed a good wash and shave, and was about to say so when the apparition vanished. Clearly the ghostly visitor preferred to maintain his grubby appearance.

An unseen something may tug at your sleeve in Upper Borough Walls. Nobody seems to know anything about this phantom and there is no story behind it. However, the Seven Stars public house which was demolished during World War II was situated in Upper Borough Walls. It was a hostelry with a very sinister reputation, believed by many to be haunted.

and gaiters. A second witness from the 1970s reported a cold feeling of unease and unpleasantness when the ghost strolled past. Reports of the man in the black hat are too numerous to mention, but his favourite trick seems to be to walk towards a witness and then vanish with unnerving suddenness. Bennett Street and Saville Row are perhaps the most fruitful hunting grounds for those who wish to see this most persistent of ghosts.

If the man in the black hat is connected with the Assembly Rooms, so is the phantom of Popjoy's Restaurant. The beautiful and elegantly dressed woman who occasionally drifts between the tables is none other than the shade of Juliana Popjoy.

ABOVE: *Behind the Assembly Rooms in Bennett Street, the ghost of the man in a black hat has been seen.*

FAR LEFT: *A dirty unshaven spectre appears near Upper Borough Walls.*

Elegant and careful of his appearance is the ghost seen more often than any other in Bath. This is the infamous man in the black hat. It is difficult for the ghost-hunter to stop at any of the city's pubs without bumping into somebody who has had experience of him. Usually seen in the streets around the Assembly Rooms, the man in the black hat seems to date from the 1770s, the time that the magnificent building was constructed.

As might be expected, his most distinguishing feature is a tall black hat with a wide brim. Most witnesses also report that he wears a large, heavy cloak wrapped tightly around him.

One witness, who saw him in Saville Row in 1974, saw the cloak billow and swirl as if in a strong wind. Underneath, the phantom had on a tight jacket with black breeches

LEFT: *Beau Nash and Juliana Popjoy were the uncrowned monarchs of fashionable Bath.*

Two Ladies in Blue

ABOVE: *The elegant interior of Popjoy's Restaurant.*

RIGHT: *A lady dressed in blue haunts 25 Queen Square.*

Juliana was the charming and faithful mistress of 'Beau Nash'. In 1705, after short periods in the army and at the bar, Richard Nash took to gambling, fashion and society as a far more congenial way of life. It was largely through his limitless talent for publicity, his good taste and the number of influential friends who visited him that Bath became the city it is.

Under the unofficial rule of Nash, Bath became the favoured watering place for the gentry and also royalty. By the time of his death in 1762 Nash had imprinted his personality on Bath; this can still be seen in the magnificent architecture of the city's houses and public buildings, one of which is the Assembly Rooms.

The building which is now Popjoy's Restaurant was built by Nash as his home, and a fine mansion it is too. Strategically located so that Nash could easily reach the more fashionable houses and entertainments, its elegant lines helped to set a new fashion in architecture.

A seemingly satisfied diner is another lady who frequents Popjoy's Restaurant. Popjoy's is better known for the phantom of Juliana, but this ghost is much more modern. To all appearances the apparition could be any well-dressed middle-aged lady who might pop in for lunch. Some people have said that her clothes are slightly 1960s for today's taste, but most notice absolutely nothing strange about the lady sitting alone; that is, until she dissolves into thin air.

Another beautiful lady of similar age, if one should ask a lady ghost such an impertinent question, is to be found at 25 Queen Square. Dressed in blue silk, the lady impresses all who see her with her elegance, beauty and slight sadness. The fact that the building is now occupied by offices rather than a family home may account for her now infrequent appearances. Efficient and computerised offices are hardly the place for the type of elegance and beauty which made 18th century Bath so famous.

Almost as tantalising is the spectre, also clad in blue, which haunts the Tudor mansion of St Catherine's Court in Batheaston. Exactly how old the lady in blue might be is difficult to say. Most witnesses only glimpse her for a second before she fades from view. Perhaps the best guess would be to place her mortal existence in around 1760, judging by the cut of her exquisite gown. On one point, all witnesses are agreed. The lady in blue is quite extraordinarily attractive.

Quite what the ghost of Julian Road looks like is unknown, but witnesses are left in no doubt about what he does. Those who pause to linger by the brick wall are taken

roughly by the shoulder and shaken violently by unseen hands. The hands are clearly powerful and give the impression of being masculine. Why the phantom should object to people leaning on the wall, however, is as unknown as his identity.

Equally obscure is the coach and four which trots around the Royal Crescent. So solid and apparently real is this coach that more than one stranger has innocently asked if a film is being shot, before being told he has seen a ghost. Local imagination has been swift, however, to link the ghostly carriage to dramatic and romantic events on 18th March 1772. Early that morning Elizabeth Linley, beautiful daughter of the owner of No.11, eloped in a similar coach with a dashing young Irishman of great talent, but little wealth, named Richard Sheridan. Thomas Linley was aghast at his daughter's behaviour, chased the young couple to France and dragged them home. He remained estranged from his new son-in-law until 1775, when young Sheridan unexpectedly penned a comedy play which became a sensation and assured his fortune. Mr Linley at once accepted him into the family.

LEFT: *A phantom coach has been seen trundling around famous Royal Crescent.*

ABOVE: *Richard Brinsley Sheridan, the famous playwright and politician.*

BELOW: *Another lady clad in blue is glimpsed occasionally in St Catherine's Court at Batheaston.*

The Sobbing Ghost

ABOVE: *An eerie sobbing has been heard in the top room of 16 Northgate Street.*

No doubt remains as to the identity of the phantom at 19 Bennett Street. So well known is this ghost that more than one visitor has travelled all the way from Australia to visit the house. Admiral Arthur Philip lived out his old age here, dying in 1814 at the age of 76. In his younger days Philip sailed with the Portuguese navy, but it was in the British navy that he achieved fame. In 1786 he was given a fleet and sent out to found a colony on the eastern coast of Australia, then only recently explored by Captain Cook. The colony he founded grew to become the city of Sydney. He was later confirmed as the first Governor of New South Wales.

A plaque to Admiral Philip can be found in the Abbey, but his ghost threatens to become even more famous than his official memorial. He is said to appear on the staircase, politely making way for ladies as they pass. The strange noises heard in No.19 are also blamed on him.

It has been reported that the admiral is the best authenticated ghost in Bath. He is small and unattractive looking, with piercing blue eyes. He wears a short cape and broad-brimmed hat.

A scandal which would undoubtedly have been known to Admiral Philip occurred at 16 Northgate Street in about 1790. The daughter of the house became pregnant by a man with no intention of honouring his promises of marriage. The unfortunate girl was ordered to leave the house by her furious father and to go to live with distant relatives in the north. The girl's aunt, a Miss Hunt, was distraught and emotions ran high. As the girl was leaving, the aunt fell from a top-floor window. Whether this was suicide, murder or an accident is unknown.

Since then poor Miss Hunt has been heard sobbing in her top-floor room or moving around the upper floors. During the 1970s and 1980s the building was occupied by a bridal shop. The unfortunate theme seems to have upset Miss Hunt who became more

active than ever. Since the shop moved, however, the hauntings have almost ceased.

A quite different tragedy led to the haunting of Batheaston Churchyard. Here a lady dressed in grey hovers near the entrance to the churchyard. It is said that she died when a coach bound for Bath from London overturned here in the late 18th century. Those passengers seeking frivolity in pleasure-loving Bath met only grief.

Equally fatal, but less unforeseen, were the events which led to the haunting of The Dell in Royal Victoria Park. Now just part of the delightful park laid out a century or so ago, this was formerly a rather wild and remote place where the reckless young men could settle their affairs of honour free of the probing eyes of those seeking to enforce Beau Nash's ban on duelling. The sound of clashing swords and a sudden penetrating chill can interrupt early morning walkers hereabouts.

Far more pleasant are the phantoms of Edward Street. One of the grander houses here has a haunted front room. When the room is empty, it echoes with the sound of stately dance music, heels tapping on wooden floorboards and the tinkle of light laughter. Clearly the phantoms of Edward Street are enjoying their lengthy sojourn on earth. But they do not enjoy company. As soon as any mortal enters the room the party breaks up in silence.

Camden Crescent is home to a sadder phantom dating back to the heyday of Bath.

One of the many private gaming clubs was established here. Two gamesters fell out over a suspect dealing of cards, and pistols were drawn in anger. The servants at once sprang forward to intervene, and one accidentally received a fatal bullet. It is his spirit which flits quietly around, perhaps to calm any angry spirits which may be present.

ABOVE: *The ghost of a victim of an overturned coach hovers near Batheaston Churchyard.*

LEFT: *Spooky noises emerge from an empty room in a house in Edward Street.*

FAR LEFT: *The spirit of a slain servant flits through a house in Camden Crescent.*

A Phantom in Uniform

Famous in history is the portly gentleman whose phantom forces his considerable presence on 71 Great Pulteney Street. This is Richard, Earl Howe, who crowned a naval career of startling success at the Battle of the Glorious First of June in 1794, when his novel tactics ensured total victory over a French fleet. After this battle, Howe retired to his home in Bath, where he lived until his death in 1799. His ghost has a limited but none-the-less commanding repertoire. He is seen most often striding around the upper floors as if looking for something. On rarer occasions he will stomp into the kitchen and take off his boots, hat and cloak to reveal an immaculate naval uniform before strolling upstairs carrying his boots.

By far the best-known ghost story of Bath centres around two fine old buildings, the Theatre Royal and the adjacent Garrick's Head pub. One fateful night many years ago, in 1812 according to one version and 1880 to another, a game of cards was going on in the Garrick's Head. Among the players were

the husband of an actress and the man suspected, rightly, of being her lover. Tempers flared over the wine and the cards. The evening ended in a wild game played for the possession of the lady, who was performing ignorant of events next door.

When the lover won the final hand, the

LEFT: *The entrance to the Theatre Royal where two sad phantoms are to be seen.*

BELOW: *The Theatre Royal and the Garrick's Head Inn. Here a fateful game of cards was once played.*

husband drew his rapier and plunged it into his rival's heart. The unfortunate wife walked in on the rumpus and hanged herself in grief.

Since that day both the victims have been seen repeatedly. The man is dressed in the height of fashion and has been described as handsome enough to turn any woman's head. The ghostly lady is rather more indistinct, but more active. She is seen repeatedly by staff and theatre-goers flitting between the two buildings. Some people have suggested that there are two ladies in grey, but most prefer the traditional version of events.

In 1979 a celebrated seance was held in the Theatre Royal at which messages, claiming to be from the grey lady, came through. Regrettably these either were nonsense or flatly contradicted all known facts, and so were of little use. Rather more worthwhile was the sponsored Spook Watch organised by girls from Bath Technical College in 1982, which succeeded in raising funds for local drama groups, although it was signally unsuccessful in raising any phantoms!

Ghosts apart, the Theatre Royal is an odd place. Every year since 1948 a tortoise-shell butterfly has visited the auditorium during the pantomime run, a season when butterflies are not generally to be found.

RIGHT: *A ghostly lady paints in an upstairs room in the Coombe Grove Hotel.*

BELOW: *Groaning and wailing is heard near the Groaning Wall.*

BELOW RIGHT: *A house in Widcombe Terrace is plagued by a dribbling, naked spook.*

A haunted locality which almost explains itself is the notorious Groaning Wall by the Mineral Water Hospital. The terrible moans of souls in pain have been heard many times by this ancient stone wall. Who is groaning and why is, unfortunately, lost in time.

More easily explained is the haunting of Coombe Grove Hotel. When the building was a private home it belonged to a lady who loved painting. She can still be seen from time to time at her easel in an upstairs room.

Less persistent, but more enigmatic, was the haunting of Citizen's House. This fine building had a reputation as an unlucky house long before Richard, Duke of Buckingham and Chandos, bought it in 1841. As Lord Privy Seal and a startlingly elegant courtier, the Duke had much to look forward to but only a few years after taking Citizen's House he was forced to relinquish his great offices and flee abroad to escape bankruptcy and scandal. It was about this time that the phantom raucous laughter and piercing screams began to echo around the building. After several more decades of misfortune, Citizen's House burnt down in 1935 and the hauntings came to an end.

RIGHT: *A ghostly lady paints in an upstairs room in the Coombe Grove Hotel.*

BELOW: *Groaning and wailing is heard near the Groaning Wall.*

PART OF THE MEDIÆVAL WALL OF THE CITY OF BATH

BELOW RIGHT: *A house in Widcombe Terrace is plagued by a dribbling, naked spook.*

WIDCOMBE TERRACE

Far more disturbing was the ghost which hit the headlines in 1974. So persistent and terrifying was this phantom that it drove a family of mere mortals from their home in Widcombe Terrace. Appearing at first rarely but with increasing frequency, the spectre was unnerving, to say the least. An elderly, overweight man who dribbles at the mouth constantly would have been bad enough, but the fact that he was nude added somewhat to the concern of the family. Hardly surprisingly, they left as soon as they could rent another home. Nor is it to be wondered at that the estate agent handling the sale denied all knowledge of the supernatural events.

York House has a more enigmatic ghost. Footsteps regularly climb the stairs and sometimes a shadowy figure of a man is glimpsed. It is said that this is the ghost of a servant of Frederick, Duke of York, who kept house here in the 1790s. According to the story repeated in Bath pubs for decades, the notoriously profligate Duke kept a mistress here for his visits to Bath and had two children by her. When the Duke spurned the mistress, it is said, she picked up with a new sponsor and left the children with the servants. Owing to a tragic misunderstanding, the ser-

vants left for London unaware that the children were locked in the house. Their pathetic starved bodies were found when the servant whose ghost remains returned some weeks later. Such stories are the stuff of gossip but no hint of such scandal can be found in the history books. This is odd, for they seem immensely fond of repeating all sorts of gossip and tales of misconduct about the Duke of York. Perhaps it is no more than an imaginative attempt to explain the phantom footsteps.

BELOW: *York House was once owned by a profligate Duke whose children starved to death.*

The Guardian of the Garden

No such doubt hangs around the old woman of Grosvenor Place. This is most certainly the ghost of the lady who lived here during the Victorian period. Her ghost began to walk within days of her death and was recognised by many friends.

Of similar vintage, or possibly slightly earlier, is Bunty the serving girl at the Beehive Inn. This cheerful soul is seen most often upstairs, probably to the relief of customers who might otherwise doubt their sobriety. She sometimes appears in the kitchen, where she will lift the lids of pans as if checking that the fare being served to customers is as good as it was in her day. Bunty is described by those who see her as emanating a great feeling of friendliness. Her smile and sparkling eyes may help the image, and several witnesses have remarked on her shiny shoes.

Equally fussy over her appearance is the lady phantom of the Grey House in Batheaston. Always fastidious about dressing in her favourite shade of purple, the lady was a keen gardener during her lifetime and was the terror of the locals she engaged to help her in her frail old age during the Edwardian

RIGHT: *Bunty the smiling kitchen maid awaits customers at the Beehive Inn.*

case was found, winding narrowly up to the room above. Thick with dust which had not been disturbed in decades, the staircase yet echoed to footsteps. Downstairs in the restaurant a man in a green jacket has been glimpsed on occasion. Whether or not this is the same ghost which climbs the blocked-off stairs is unknown. Though the history of the house is well known, there has been none of the highly emotional dramas which usually lie behind hauntings. The man's origin is a mystery.

Boasting an identity is the ghost of Burlington Street. This well-dressed lady was the wife of an Edwardian vicar. She became famous for her tea parties to which were invited the cream of local society. It is therefore no wonder that her ghost is seen most often at around four in the afternoon; looking for cucumber sandwiches, no doubt.

ABOVE: *An unknown ghost in a top hat haunts the steak house in Queen Street.*

RIGHT: *Four o'clock in the afternoon is ghost-time in Burlington Street.*

era. Death did little to change her character. For many years after her demise she would appear waving furiously at any garden staff who dared take a crafty rest or tried some short-cut in their work. She has not been seen in recent years, so perhaps she is happy with the present gardeners. Woe betide any new contractors who fall below their standards.

The steak house at 8 Queen Street not only serves tasty meals, but also boasts a fine ghost, perhaps two. For years the ladies' powder room was plagued by phantom footsteps which sounded as if they were climbing stairs, and by a shadowy male figure in what appeared to be a top hat. When redecoration was undertaken on this 250 year-old building in 1981, a hollow panel was found in the powder room. When this was removed, in true ghost story fashion, a walled-in stair-

Queens Square is home to a far sadder spectre. This is the shade of Sylvia, a young Victorian lady who was spurned by her fiancé just days before the wedding. The distraught girl hanged herself in her wedding finery and now returns to flit around the square as a lady in white.

The gravel path leading to Brock Street is the haunt of a tall man with grey hair. He is reported to be dressed in a lounge suit of somewhat old-fashioned cut and the best guess is that he dates from the 1930s. This spectre is seen so often that he has ceased to cause either alarm or interest, and must rival the nearby man in the black hat for the title of most active ghost in Bath.

Seen less often is the man with a ribbon in his hair. Most descriptions agree that this is a gentleman dressed in the height of mid-18th century fashion. His powdered wig is drawn back into a bun by the ribbon and his long coat is heavily embroidered. Visible only to men, the phantom is fussy about appearing, and does so only rarely.

BELOW: *The spirit of a jilted girl wanders round Queen Square.*

Never seen at all are the ghosts of No. 8, now occupied by the Royal College of Nursing. They are heard, however, many times. The sound of conversation coming from the drawing room is usually quite friendly and jovial, but it stops whenever a living person enters. This was formerly the home of Mrs Piazzi, who saw Bath in its finest days during her lifetime of 1741 to 1821. Perhaps the festive phantoms are those of Mrs Piazzi and her guests.

Trim Street can boast an equally obscure phantom. Described most often as a shadowy form, but sometimes as a man in grey, this spectre is seen gliding silently along the street at various times of day.

The ghostly lady in the Circus was only seen twice that anybody can recall. The first time was just one week after her funeral in the 1880s, when the little lady hobbled up to her front door, just as she had done on so many occasions when alive, though on this occasion her family were rather more surprised to see her. The second sighting was a few weeks later, and she has not been seen since.

LEFT: *The gravel path near Gay Street where the figure of a man dressed in the fashion of the 1930s has been seen.*

BELOW LEFT: *Trim Street is haunted by the shadowy form of a man dressed in grey.*

BELOW: *A lady called at a house in the Circus a week after her funeral.*

ABOVE: *A smiling butler greets visitors to a house in Cold Ashton and then vanishes.*

RIGHT: *A porter at the Registry of Births, Marriages and Deaths was noticed frequently after his death knocking on the door at 10.30 a.m.*

Much more solid is the phantom butler of Cold Ashton, an outlying village. Here there is a large house approached by a massive wooden gate set between pillars adorned with stone urns of fruit. If you have reason to call, you need to look carefully at whoever opens the door. If it is an elderly man dressed in a black tail-coat who smiles engagingly and asks your business, you may have met the phantom butler. You will know for certain if he vanishes a few seconds later. This ghost seems to have been most active during the 1930s when several reports were made, but seemingly has since faded.

Knocking on another door, that of the Registry of Births, Marriages and Deaths in Charles Street, is the phantom of Ebenezer Ash. He was a porter here in Victorian days when the building was a bank. Renowned for his punctuality, Ebenezer was never late for work, appearing promptly at 10.30 every morning. After his death in 1888 his phantom continued to knock on the door precisely at 10.30. These days his ghost is rarely seen and the knock is becoming less frequent.

Just six years after Ebenezer Ash passed away, Bath experienced a curious happening which has never been explained. Thousands of small jellyfish dropped from a rain cloud. Surprised citizens had little choice but to sweep the mess up and wonder how all the jellyfish got there.

A phantom just as insistent as Ebenezer Ash stalks through Milsom Street. In 1928 old Josiah Burns passed away. His last years had been spent in some poverty and one of Josiah's main preoccupations was to save money, particularly by wrapping himself up instead of burning coal and by switching off all lights whenever possible. Ever since his death the various shops and flats in Milsom Street have experienced strange goings-on. Lights will be flicked off for no apparent reason, heating will be turned down and electric appliances of all kinds will be switched off by no human hand. It can only be presumed that old Josiah believes he is doing the present-day occupants a favour by saving them money, but to be suddenly plunged into chill darkness can be most inconvenient.

Almost as troublesome is Arthur Foster who has refused to leave the Salamander Inn. Arthur was one of the most habitual regulars at the Salamander prior to his death before the last war. He remains a regular, though his visits are today less frequent and more dramatic. His well-known hobnail boots will crunch their way across the bar, though nobody is moving, and if things are not just as he likes them, he will rearrange glasses, ornaments and furniture. He must have been devoted indeed to return not only after pub hours, but also after his own.

LEFT: *The crunch of hob-nailed boots have been heard in the bar of the Salamander Inn.*

A Poltergeist Strikes

Troublesome in a different way is No.21 Royal Crescent which, if local gossip is to be believed, does not like women. Quite why a house should take a dislike to the female sex is difficult to know, but women owners have rarely been happy here. The latest event to become newsworthy occurred in 1975 when London-based artist Jennifer Neelands bought the house, but had to sell it almost at once when she found it impossible to stay there. Former lady owners to enjoy ill luck included Marianne Hare, aunt of writer Augustus Hare, who as a young woman enjoyed a flirtatious romance with an obscure French army officer whom she left for what appeared a safer marriage opportunity. The unknown officer was named Napoleon Bona-

BELOW: 21 Royal Crescent dislikes being owned by a woman.

parte and poor Marianne spent her old age in Bath bemoaning her decision to anybody who would listen.

Dramatic indeed was the poltergeist of Camley Green, Twerton, which struck in 1975. Outwardly an ordinary council house, No.61 Camley Green lurched to national fame in April 1975 when the family was moved by the Council to another home following an escalation in the haunting. In addition to the more normal poltergeist activity of bangs, thumps and moving furniture the ghost which plagued the Oliver family managed to produce spots of intense cold and to send family members into trance-like comas.

Since the Olivers left, the house has been entirely peaceful. The tenants who took over the lease found the house extremely pleasant.

More determined to stick things out were the tenants of a house in Gay Street which similarly found itself in the news in 1976. Outsiders first heard of the strange events when the police were called by a badly shaken Giuseppe Merolla, who ran the Italian restaurant on the ground floor. One night he heard what he thought was a body fall on the floor above and then heavy dragging noises. Fearing the worst, he armed himself with a carving knife before making his way to the phone and calling for help.

Only then was it revealed that the accountants who occupied the upstairs offices had been experiencing similar problems for some time. After dark, staff were regularly reporting strange noises and lights being switched on and off by unseen hands. A student helping out with late night filing found herself face to face with a shapeless thing which glided along a corridor. The problem was eventually solved by the pragmatic arrangement of banning overtime after dark. The phantom was simply left to get on with its activities free of human interference. Presumably it still does.

A spectre met a more ignominious fate at the hands of the police in 1977. The Nunney Road, running out of the city to the south, was for many years famous for its phantom hitch-hiker. The middle-aged man dressed in smart tweeds would flag vehicles down as if wanting a lift, but would unaccountably vanish if anybody stopped. Local pranksters decided to take advantage of the haunting and set up an elaborate hoax. A cut-out figure was painted on to cardboard and suspended from a tree, being lowered on wires when a car approached, but whipped up out of sight if the vehicle stopped. Police were on to the hoax straightaway and impounded the fake spectre, though they never caught the human culprits. Meanwhile the genuine spectre continues his odd game of hide-and-seek with the travelling public.

So it is with all the ghosts of Bath. Human investigators, tourists and ghosthunters may come and go, but the ghosts continue their own mysterious ways unhindered. Be it the beautiful lady in blue of Batheaston, the gory soldier on Freezing Hill or the persistent Ebenezer Ash, the spectral inhabitants of Bath are every bit as real as the living. And if you miss the man in the black hat, there is always the magnificent architecture and fine tea rooms to help you enjoy your time in this elegant city.

LEFT: *Two different phantoms have been glimpsed in the vicinity of Gay Street.*

BELOW: *A poltergeist is said to have caused the dragging noises which troubled the residents of 61 Camley Green.*

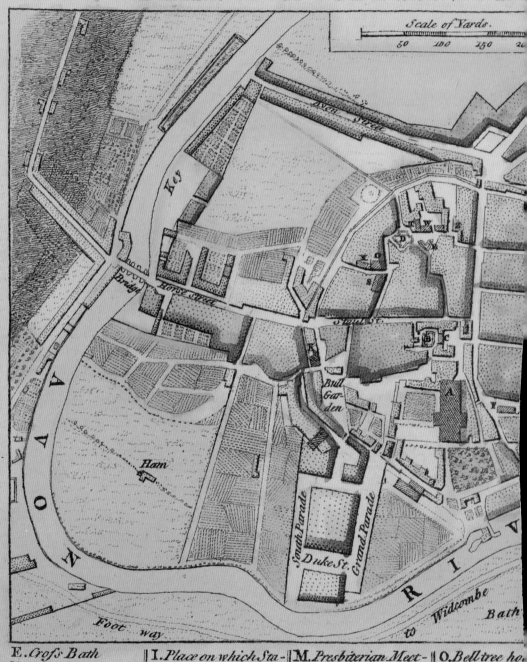

PLAN of the CITY and SUB

E. *Cross Bath*
F. *Town Hall*
G. *General Hospital*
H. *St. Marys Church*

I. *Place on which Sta-*
uls Church stood
K. *St. James's Church*
L. *St. Michaels Church*

M. *Presbiterian Meet-*
ing house
N. *Quakers Meeting-*
house

O. *Bell tree ho*
P. *an Obelisk*
Q. *a Pyramid*
R. *Cold Bath*